TOTALLY TWISTED PUZZLES

DEFINITELY NOT FOR AARDVARKS!

Hi, I'm Aardvark. Keep an eye out for me as you work through this book!

You may have spotted that this is not a normal puzzle book – it's a TOTALLY TWISTED puzzle book.

Some puzzles are easy and some are hard but beware, things are not always what they seem! Keep your wits about you. You'll need all the wits you can get!

This book is definitely not for aardvarks, well, apart from me, but then I am TOTALLY TWISTED...

Before you start, check out the CHICKEN EGG CODE. You'll need this for some of the puzzles but hey, why not use it with your friends to send each other top secret messages?

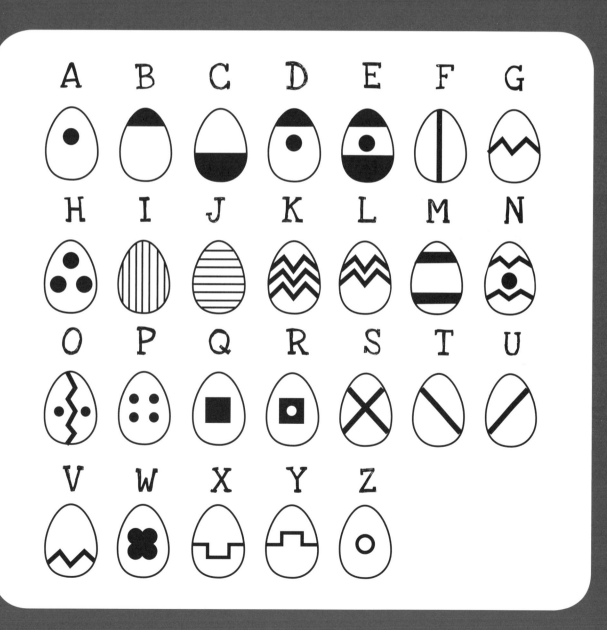

THE HIDDEN ME

Draw your portrait below.

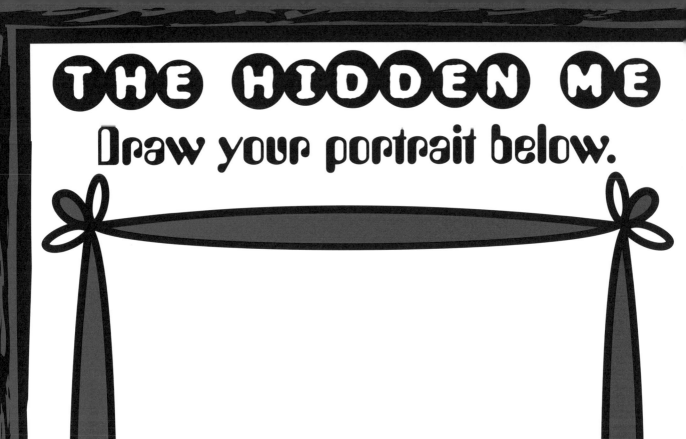

Your name in
chicken egg code is

- -

DRAW WHERE YOU GO TO SCHOOL...

...upside down without turning the book!

Can you guess who is the odd one out?

2

How many fingers and thumbs can you count?

3

Finish these peeping patterns.

1

2

3

4

Those eyes seem to follow you around!

Drift off in a daydream and see what you doodle.

PICTURE PUZZLER!

This confused artist needs a hand.
Put the stages of the picture in order.

Which shadow belongs to this frog?

1

2

3

7

8 How many circles can you see in this pattern?

GET TO THE BEACH NOW!

9

Connect the dots to discover what this is.

DOODLE THE TIME AWAY...

tra la la....
la la....

Copy this cool cat using the hand you don't normally write with.

WHICH IS THE ODD GHOST OUT?

1 2 3 4 5

6 7 8

13

They all look odd to me!

What is hiding in this pile of leaves?

14

Draw a totally twisted doodle!

MAKE A FUNNY FACE AND DRAW IT HERE.

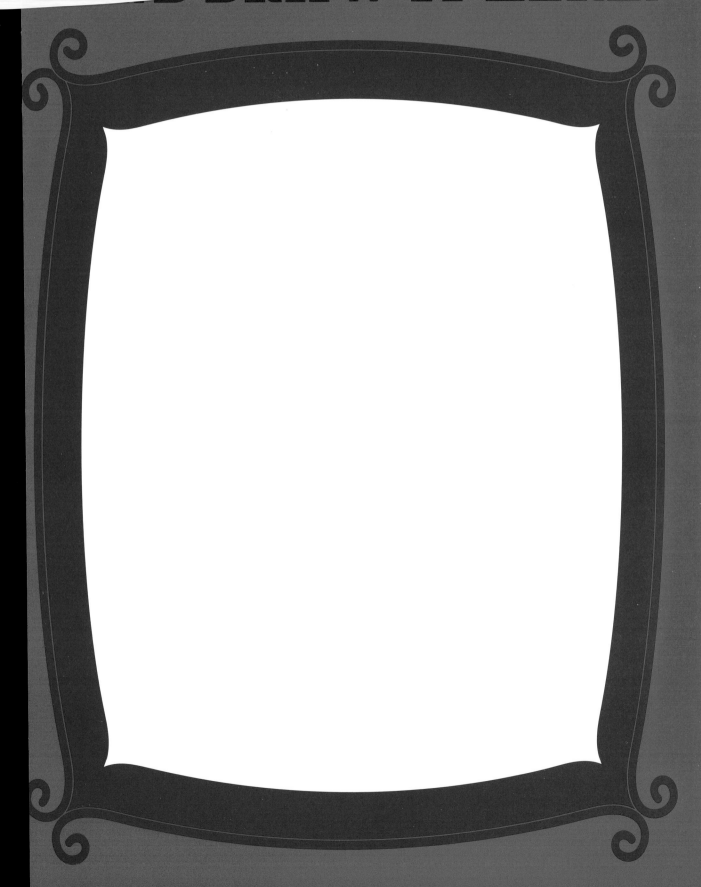

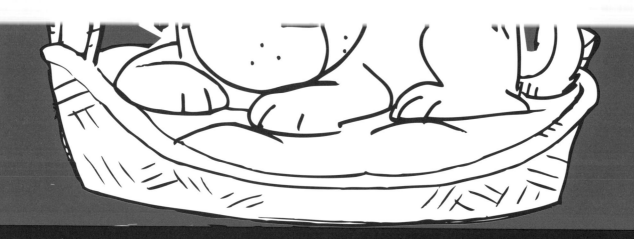

Pair up the twin dogs.

1

2

3

A

B

C

18

Which two halves make this boy's shadow?

How many starfish can you see?

ch path leads to the sheep?

WHAT TOTALLY TWISTED THINGS ARE HAPPENING IN THIS PICTURE?

Draw your own totally twisted animal mash-up.

Finish these patterns.

 **1**

 **2**

 **3**

25

WHO is this person looking at?

What picture do these pieces make?

CLOSED

Who are they?

- - - - - - - - - - - - - - -

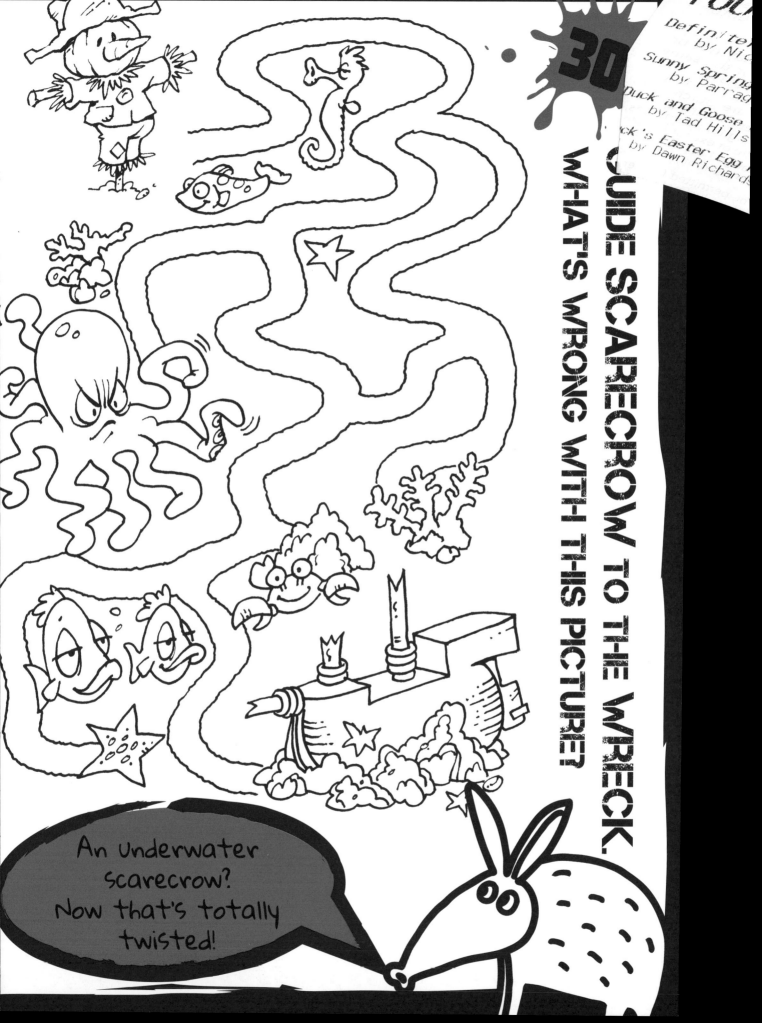

GUIDE SCARECROW TO THE WRECK.

WHAT'S WRONG WITH THIS PICTURE?

An underwater scarecrow? Now that's totally twisted!

Finish drawing
this picture
with your
eyes closed.

WHAT IS THIS A SHADOW OF?

Clue: It'll put a smile on your face!

Help Count DRACULA count his bats.
What would happen if all the bats flew away?

DRAW SOMETHING WITHOUT TAKING YOUR PENCIL OFF THE PAPER...

FOLLOW THE LINES TO SEE WHAT TOTALLY TWISTED GIFTS THESE CHILDREN ARE GETTING.

Copy the grid square by square and draw the ZEBRA the correct way up.

What's wrong with this picture?

34

Which shadow matches the backpack?

35

1   2   3

Help the PIRATES sort out their TREASURE...

How many coins have the pirates found? ☐ ①

If 2 pirates share the treasure how many coins are left over? ☐ ②

If 3 pirates take 6 coins each, how many are left over? ☐ ③

Draw lines to match the pairs. Which are the odd ones out?

DOODLE SOMETHING REALLY, REALLY AWESOME!

Turn this face into a famous movie star. Can your friends guess who it is?

CONNECT THE DOTS TO SEE THE PICTURE.

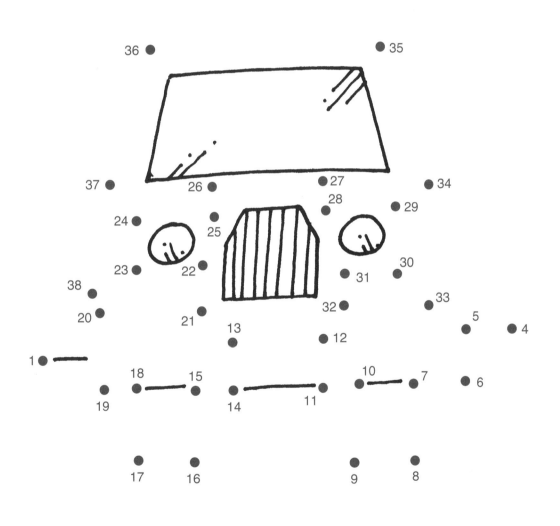

Piece the shadows together to reveal two tea-riffic things this girl has dropped.

HOW MANY SCARVES CAN YOU SEE?

40

TOTALLY TWISTED! AND MORE ...

Doodle your favorite foods...

...all on one plate!

Draw a line to match these heads to their bodies.

41

DRAW IN THE MISSING DOMINOES TO FINISH EACH SEQUENCE...

42

MAKE A SCARY FACE IN THE MIRROR... DRAW IT HERE.

Aargh!

DOODLE SOMETHING YOU SEE IN THE CLOUDS.

CAN YOU SEE FIVE AARDVARKS HiDiNG?

Use the chicken egg code to find what colors you need to color the snowman.

1  _____

2  _____

3 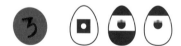 _____

4  _____

5  _____

6  _____

Put the pieces in order to make a robot.

45

NEED HELP WITH YOUR HOMEWORK OR DOING CHORES?

Design your very own robot helper.

Copy this BAT

How many EYEBALLS are staring at you?

46

¡umop ǝpᴉsdn

WHICH PICTURE COMPLETES OUR SUPERHERO JIGSAW?

47

If you were an AARDVARK, what would you draw?

Draw a MIRROR image of this BOAT.

Which HEAD is thinking about the most BONES?

HOW MANY BALLS IS THIS CLOWN JUGGLING?

49

Connect the dots to reveal the picture.

50

Which creature has eight long legs?

Doodle something beginning with 'T'.

Which FRUIT is the ODD one OUT?

51

HOW MANY OF THESE NUMBERS CAN YOU FIND?

52

7 ☐

3 ☐

9 ☐

If this spinning TOP looks exactly the same all around, how many CIRCLES does it have?

53

54

LAST MINUTE DOODLE DASH...

ANSWERS

1. Number 4 because he's the only one wearing dark glasses.

2. 36 fingers, 9 thumbs.

3.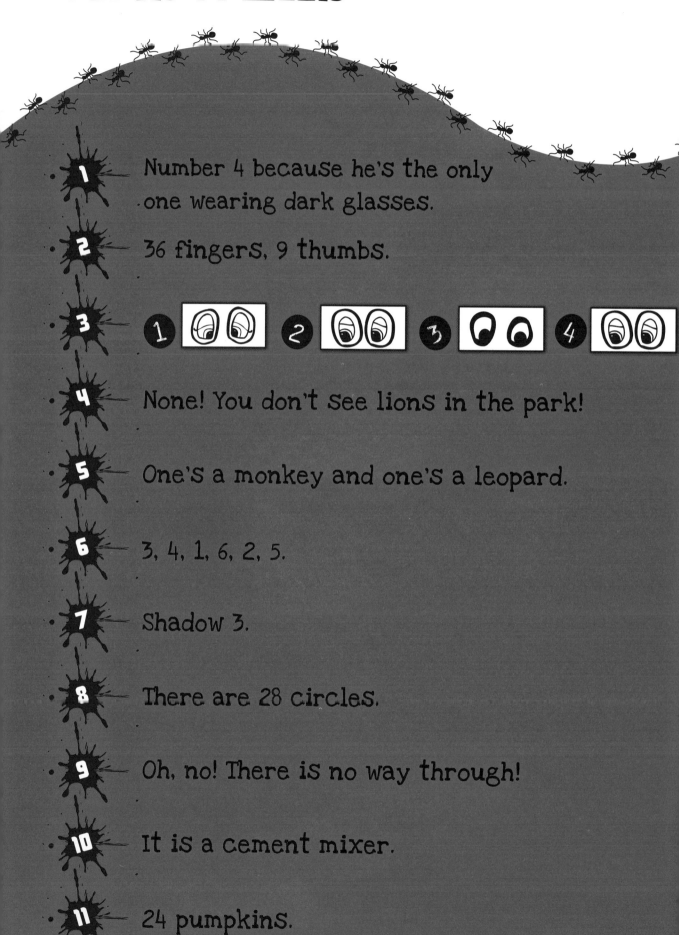

4. None! You don't see lions in the park!

5. One's a monkey and one's a leopard.

6. 3, 4, 1, 6, 2, 5.

7. Shadow 3.

8. There are 28 circles.

9. Oh, no! There is no way through!

10. It is a cement mixer.

11. 24 pumpkins.

12 — It's the wrong shadow!

13 — Number 7.

14 — Can't see, because it's hiding!

15 — There are 20 diamond shapes.

16 — 1. b, 2. d, 3. a, 4. c.

17 — Can't see any! They're too small.

18 — They're all the same!

19 — 2 and 3.

20 — There are 20 starfish.

21 — They all do!

22 — Balloons in the sky, dino wearing hat, dino eating banana, and cat with food bowl.

23 A koala, a spider, and a duck.

24 Can't see! It's too dark.

25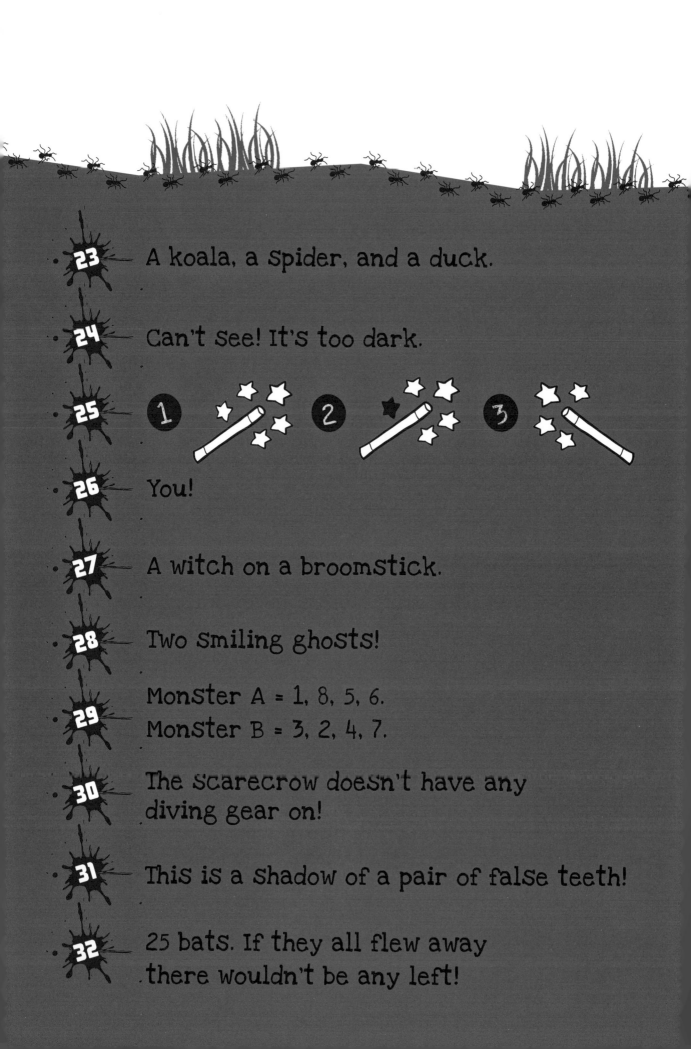

26 You!

27 A witch on a broomstick.

28 Two smiling ghosts!

29 Monster A = 1, 8, 5, 6.
Monster B = 3, 2, 4, 7.

30 The scarecrow doesn't have any diving gear on!

31 This is a shadow of a pair of false teeth!

32 25 bats. If they all flew away there wouldn't be any left!

33 — 1-A, 2-C , 3-B.

34 — Cats can't write!

35 — Number 3 is the correct shadow.

36 — 1. 30 coins, 2. 0 coins, 3. 12 coins.

37 — Pairs are 1-D, 2-A, 3-B, 5-C.
Odd ones out are 4 and E.

38 — It's a big truck.

39 — 1 and 3 = a teacup.
2 and 4 = a teapot.

40 — 9 scarves.

41 — 1. C, 2. A, 3. B.

42 —

43

44 The colors are: 1. yellow, 2. black, 3. red, 4. blue, 5. orange, 6. brown.

45 4, 2, 1, 6, 5, 3.

46 16 are looking at you. Spooky!

47 Picture number 1.

Bye for now... Hope you had lots of totally twisted fun!

48 Dog number 3. Greedy!

49 None, he's dropped them all!

50 It's an octopus, of course!

51 The apple because it doesn't grow in a bunch.

52 7-6, 3-6, 9-8.

53 6

54 Hope you had some TOTALLY TWISTED fun. Now check out your answers!